HOPSCOTCH
MYTHS

Gelert
the Brave

First published in 2008 by
Franklin Watts
338 Euston Road
London
NW1 3BH

Franklin Watts Australia
Level 17/207 Kent Street
Sydney
NSW 2000

A CIP catalogue record for this book is available
from the British Library.

ISBN 978 0 7496 7999 6 (hbk)
ISBN 978 0 7496 8007 7 (pbk)

Series Editor: Melanie Palmer
Series Advisor: Dr Barrie Wade
Series Designer: Peter Scoulding

Printed in China

Franklin Watts is a division of
Hachette Children's Books,
an Hachette Livre UK company
www.hachettelivre.co.uk

Gelert
the Brave

by Barrie Wade and Peter Utton

W
FRANKLIN WATTS
LONDON•SYDNEY

Once there was a lord who
lived in a castle on a hill.
He loved to go hunting.

The lord had many hunting dogs
but Gelert was his favourite.
He always took Gelert with
him as he was the best hunter.

The lord and Gelert spent many days hunting together in the forest. They always had lots of fun.

One morning, the lord got ready to
go hunting. Gelert ran to his side.
"No, Gelert, not you," said the lord.

"Stay here and guard my son,"
he ordered. So Gelert lay down
by the baby's cot.

It was quiet in the castle when the lord left, but Gelert sensed danger. Then a huge wolf appeared and crept right up to the baby's cot.

As the wolf came closer to the cot,
Gelert jumped at its throat.

The wolf twisted away. It dug
its teeth deep into Gelert's side.

Gelert scratched at the wolf's face and bit one of its paws. Angrily the wolf flung Gelert into the cot, knocking it over. The baby fell out.

As the wolf tried to reach the
baby, Gelert bit deep into its
throat. The wolf limped away.

Gelert crawled back to the broken
cot and lay next to the sleeping
baby. There was blood everywhere.

Then the lord came back. "Here,
Gelert! Here, boy!" he called.

Gelert heard his master shouting but he was too weak to respond.

The lord marched into the hall
and saw the dreadful mess.
The cot was knocked over and
his baby son was missing.

Then he saw Gelert with blood around his mouth!

The lord raised his sword in fury and thrust it deep into Gelert's body. The dog sank down dead.

Suddenly, the lord heard a tiny cry.
He looked behind the cot and saw
his baby son.

Then his men entered the hall.
They pointed to a wolf's body
under the table.

At once everything was clear.
Gelert had not killed the child.
Instead the brave dog had
guarded the child with his life.

The lord wept for Gelert and
promised to honour him.

The lord built a special grave for Gelert. Everyone in the land came to honour the faithful hunting dog.

People can still visit Gelert's grave today and read all about Gelert the Brave.

Hopscotch has been specially designed to fit the requirements of the National Literacy Strategy. It offers real books by top authors and illustrators for children developing their reading skills. There are 63 Hopscotch stories to choose from:

* hardback